MY FIRST STICKERS

Things that Go

Have fun completing the activities
in this vehicle-themed book!

✳

Use your pencils to colour, doodle and
complete the activities on each page.

✳

Where there is a missing sticker, you will see
an empty shape. Search your sticker pages
to find the missing sticker.

You can also press out a cool puzzle
and bookmarks from your card pages.

make
believe
ideas

On the road

Who can you see on the road? Find the missing stickers.

Beep!
Beep!

Beep!

Join the dots to complete the truck.

Vroom!

Terrific tractor

Help the farmer get home by guiding the tractor through the maze.

Chug! Chug!

Start

Sticker the missing hay bales.

Finish

3

Brilliant boats

Use colour and stickers to finish the boats.

What shapes can you see?

Digging dirt

Find the missing digger.
Then, copy and colour
to make the diggers match.

All aboard!

Use your rectangle stickers to complete the train. Which colours will you choose?

6

Choo!

Choo!

How many wheels can you see? Write the answer.

Whirring helicopter

Ellie is flying the helicopter.
Trace the clouds and find
the missing stickers.

Balloon race

Colour the other half of the hot-air balloon to match.

Sticker colourful spots on the hot-air balloon.

Noisy road

Finish colouring the vehicles on the noisy road.

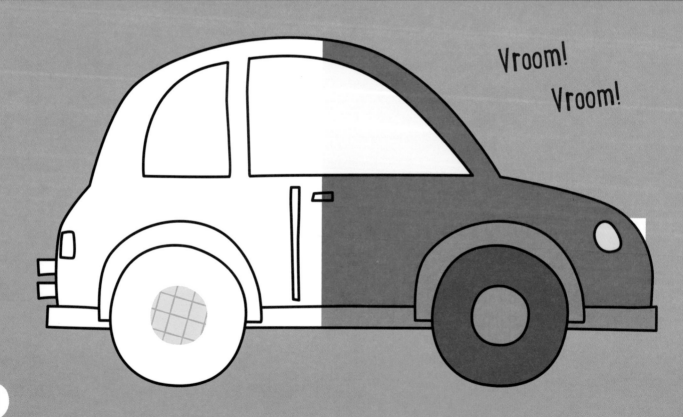

Vroom!

Vroom!

11

Farmer fun

Join the dots to finish
Farmer Fred's tractor,
and then colour it in.

Baa!

Add the
missing sticker.

Whoosh!

Sticker the missing shapes to make the balloons look beautiful.

See you soon!

Add stickers to finish the busy bus!

How many circles can you see? Write the answer.

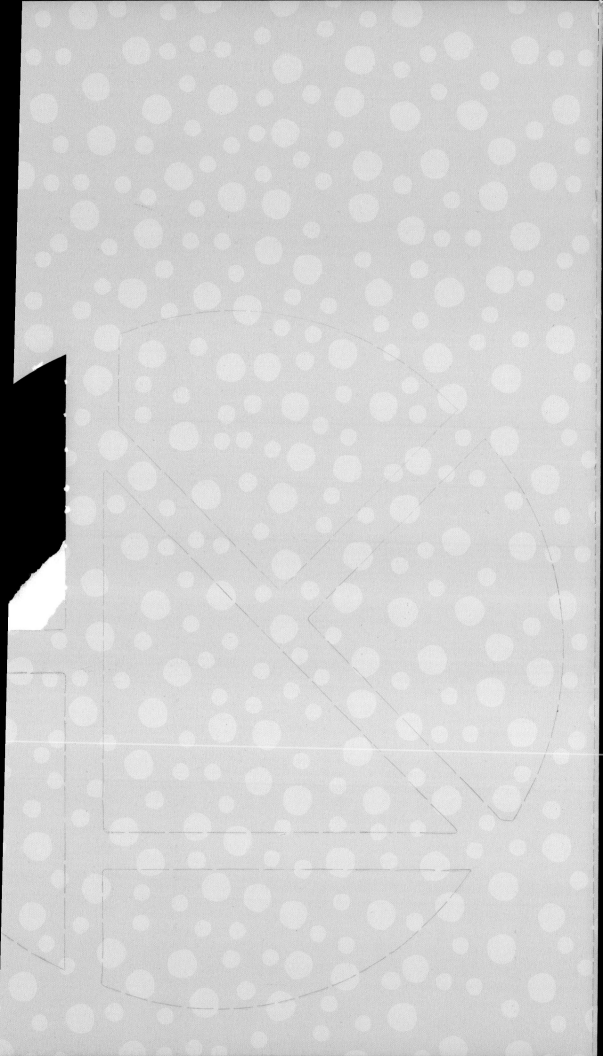

Press out the puzzle pieces. Now try to put the pieces back together to make this picture of a tooting train!

Fast-track bookmarks!

Press out and decorate the bookmarks.

Stickers for page 2

Page 3

Page 4

Page 5

Pages 6-7

Page 8

Page 9

Page 10-11

Page 12

Page 13

Pages 14-15

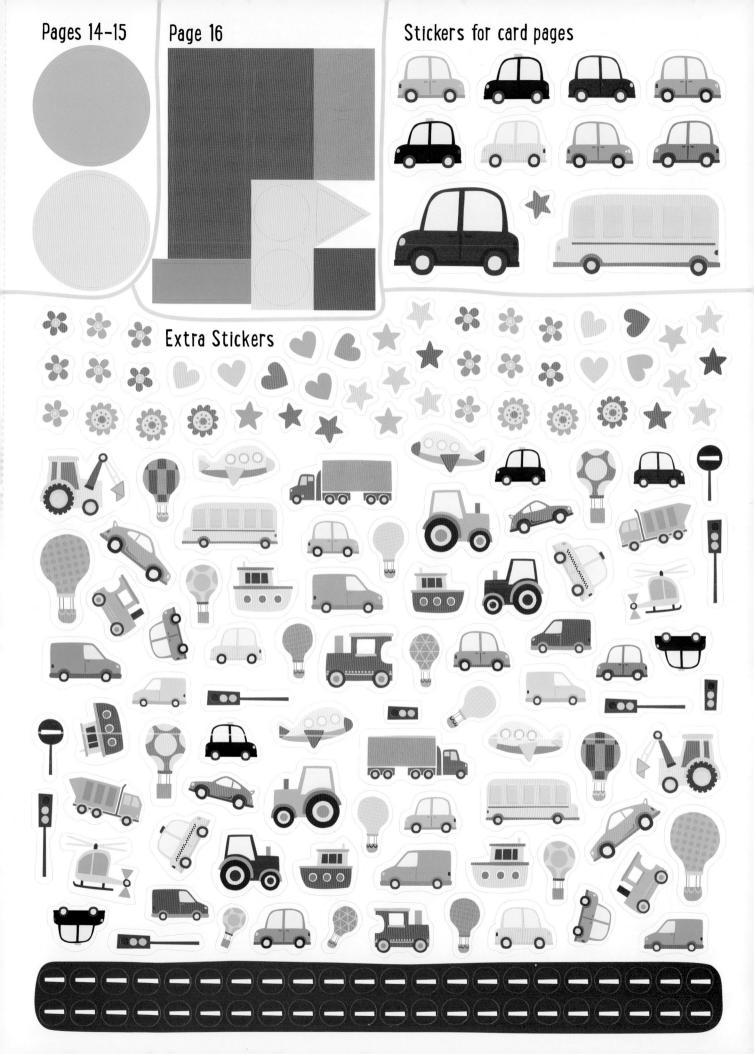

Pages 14-15

Page 16

Stickers for card pages

Extra Stickers